PUZZLES &
BRAINTEASERS

imagineTHAT!™

Imagine That! is an imprint of Top That! Publishing Inc.
25031 W. Avenue Stanford, Suite #60,
Valencia, CA 91355
www.topthatpublishing.com
Copyright © 2005 Top That! Publishing Inc.
Imagine That! is a trademark of Top That! Publishing Inc.

Contents

Introduction

At times fiendishly difficult but always worthwhile and rewarding, these puzzles and brainteasers will keep you occupied for hours on end.

With an impressive variety of puzzles and mental challenges you'll be giving your neglected gray matter a full workout. Just remember, your brain needs the attention of regular exercise as much as any other organ in your body—so get comfortable and get ready to take on the challenge!

Celebrity Wordmatch

Find a word that can follow the word on the left and precede the word on the right. When you have filled in all the answers, the name of a celebrity can be read from top to bottom in the shaded line.

CANDID							
CHIP							MAN
DARK							ROOM
HIGH							POWER
FIRST							BLADES
ROMAN							BROTHER
CARD							STICK
BLUE							TENNIS
SLEEPING							MYSTERY
PANAMA							SPOT
LIBERTY							BOAT
PAPER							RIPPER
							MARGIN

Impossipuzzle

Which is the smallest ten-digit number to be five times the cube of one number and also three times the fifth power of another?

The committee voted for three candidates. Susie got two thirds of the votes, Vera got a quarter, and Emily got the remaining three votes. How many voted?

Joe bought 296 ties of three different styles for just $296. For each style, the price in cents was the same as the number of ties he was able to get in that style. What were the prices?

Clockword

The solutions from 1 to 12 are all six-letter words ending with the letter D in the middle. Moving clockwise from 1, the letters in the outer circle will spell out the name of an English actress.

1. Technique
2. Be imminent
3. Required
4. Jogged
5. Scratched
6. Increase
7. Order
8. Plump
9. Land mass surrounded by water
10. Diverse
11. Followed
12. Consider

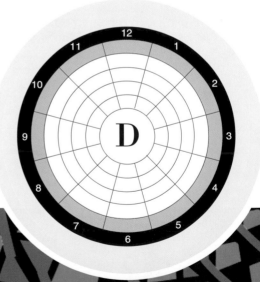

Mini Quiz

1. Which sailing ship was named after a witch in a Robert Burns poem?

2. Of which island does Haiti form the western part?

3. Which late US comedian was born Benjamin Kubelsky?

4. In which constellation is Regulus the brightest star?

5. Which American state's motto is "Friendship"?

Codeword

Codeword is the crossword puzzle with no clues. The number in each square corresponds to a letter. You have to figure out the words in the grid, using the three letters provided. Fill in these known letters first, then use your skill and judgment to work out the remainder.

1	2	3 P	4 R	5 A	6	7	8	9	10	11	12	13
14	15	16	17	18	19	20	21	22	23	24	25	26

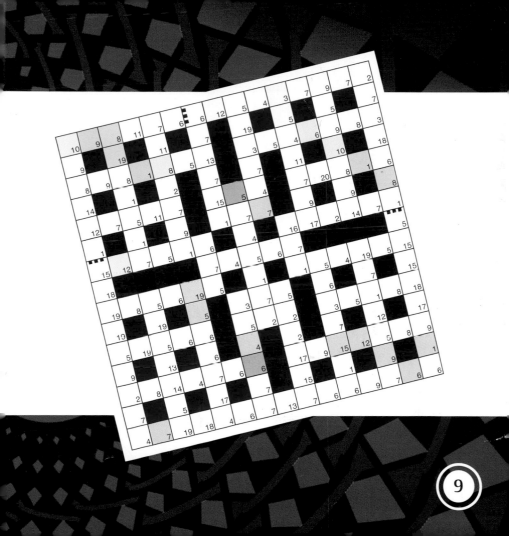

9

Word Wise

The words below may sound familiar, but do you know what they mean?

GILLIE

A A female ferret

B A Scottish manservant

C A stream

VOLITION

A Exercise one's will

B Flight

C A calling

BRISKET

A Coarse swine hair

B A block of compressed coal

C A joint of meat

PREVARICATE

A Evade the truth

B Forestall

C Anticipate

Clockword

The solutions from 1 to 12 are all six-letter words ending with the letter N in the middle. Moving clockwise from 1, the letters in the outer circle will spell out the name of a US pop singer/songwriter.

1. Fish
2. Inn
3. Cricket team
4. Instrument
5. Congenital
6. Command
7. Caretaker
8. Parentless child
9. Idea
10. Fruit
11. Flag
12. Dried grape

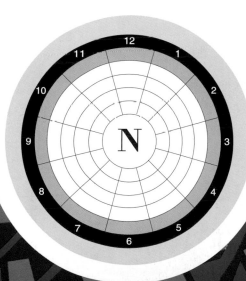

Crossword

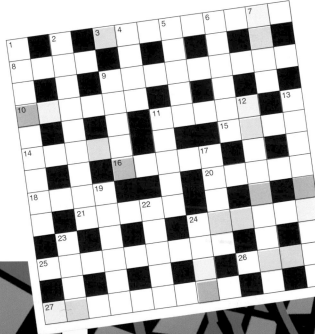

ACROSS

3. See 18 across.
8. The --- Eireann is the lower chamber of parliament in the Republic of Ireland. (4)
9 and 24 across. Novel by Charles Dickens featuring the character John Harmon. (3,6,6)
10. The tree *Prunus amygdalus*, which has an oval-shaped, edible, nut-like seed. (6)
11. In Greek mythology, father of Hector, Paris and Cassandra. (5)
14. --- *the Otter*, 1927 novel by Henry Williamson. (5)
15. --- Pompilius, legendary second King of Rome. (4)
16. Former capital of Nigeria on the Bight of Benin. (5)
18 and 3 across. *The ---*, 1985 novel by Doris Lessing. (4,9)
20. George, actor who played Mr. Sulu in *Star Trek*. (5)
21. Eudora, American author of *Delta Wedding*. (5)
24. See 9 across
25. 1651 work by Thomas Hobbes. (9)
26. Small parrot of Australia and Indonesia. (4)
27. Joop, cyclist who won the 1980 Tour de France. (9)

DOWN

1. The point after deuce in tennis. (9)
2. Actor father of the actress Jennifer Jason Leigh. (3,6)
4. Mr. Barak, former Israeli prime minister. (4)
5. Mrs. Godden, author of *Black Narcissus*. (5)
6. Climbing palm with tough stems used for wickerwork. (6)
7. Herring-like food fish of the genus Alosa. (4)
9. See 22 down.
11. Character in the novel *Lord of the Flies*. (5)
12. Variety of the vine plant *Cucumis melo* such as the cantaloupe and honeydew. (9)
13. 1987 Woody Allen movie starring Mia Farrow. (5,4)
17. Isaac, Russian-born violinist who made his New York debut in 1937. (5)
19. Jan, chief minister of the United Provinces of the Netherlands 1653-72. (2,4)
22 and 9 down. Best Supporting Actress Oscar winner for *Paper Moon*. (5,5)
23. City in Nevada famous for its divorces. (4)
24. *The ---*, 1956 novel by Albert Camus. (4)

13

Numberword

Numberword is a crossword without words—instead, it uses numbers.
See if you can complete it without using a calculator

ACROSS

5. Year of King George V of Great Britain's coronation.
7. 19 x 13112
11. 23 squared
12. 5 x 14803
13. 8 x 24727
15. End of Russo-Japanese War.
16. 3285 x 8
17. Year of first modern Olympic games.
19. Year of Earl Mountbatten's assassination.
21. 234 squared
24. Year Nasser nationalized Suez Canal.
27. 11926 x 12
29. 2 to the power of 16
31. 9 to the power of 3
32. 48444 x 3
33. Year of Muhammad Ali's last professional fight.

DOWN

1. Year of Cuban revolution.
2. 6 x 103311
3. 32 to the power of 3
4. Year Queen Victoria died.
6. 3 x 4243
8. Square root of 1936
9. 2737 divided by 23
10. 2783 x 9
14. Number of apostles.
18. 11852 x 7
19. 13 x 11824
20. 10681 x 9
22. 1892 x 22
23. Square root of 5476
25. 3885 divided by 7
26. 33 x 198
28. Year Henry Moore died.
30. Square root of 1089

Word Puzzle

The cities listed below all have famous rivers running through them. The rivers are hidden in our word grid. Can you find all ten? Words are written horizontally and vertically, not diagonally or backward.

THE CITIES

1. Vienna
2. Paris
3. Glasgow
4. Rotterdam
5. London
6. Hamburg
7. Dublin
8. Rome
9. Geneva
10. Cairo

R	E	A	R	H	O	N	E	S	A
H	R	B	T	O	R	E	D	A	C
I	G	O	R	L	N	R	O	Y	L
N	A	N	O	L	I	F	F	E	Y
E	N	C	D	I	L	M	N	V	D
X	T	H	A	M	E	S	T	I	E
F	I	R	N	U	N	G	L	E	C
N	B	O	U	R	S	E	I	N	E
G	E	L	B	E	N	G	N	T	N
P	R	E	E	S	T	R	I	O	K

Mini Quiz

1. Which record company was founded in Detroit by Berry Gordy Jnr?

2. Which fish's young include alevins and smolts?

3. What is the largest city in Switzerland?

4. In which country was Vivien Leigh born?

5. Who wrote *Cat's Cradle* in 1963?

Codeword

Codeword is the crossword puzzle with no clues.

The number in each square corresponds to a letter. You have to work out the words in the grid, using the three letters provided.

Fill in these known letters first, then use your skill and judgment to work out the remainder.

1 N	2 A	3	4	5	6	7 T	8	9	10	11	12	13
14	15	16	17	18	19	20	21	22	23	24	25	26

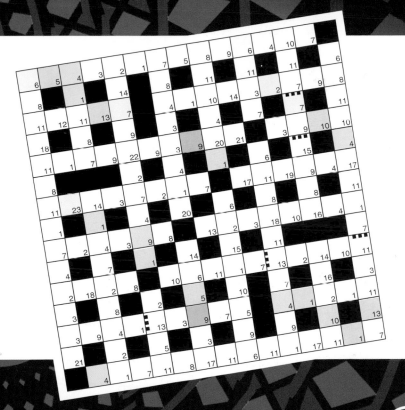

19

Word Scrambler

D I G E S T

How many words can you make from the word **DIGEST**? You have fifteen minutes to find as many as possible. Words must be at least three letters long. Plurals and multiple forms of the same verb are acceptable, but proper nouns and hyphenated words are not allowed.

13 words—good
20 words—great
26 words or more—fantastic

How many words can you make from the word **TROWEL**? Once again, you have fifteen minutes to find as many as possible. Words must be at least three letters long. Plurals and multiple forms of the same verb are permitted as before, but proper nouns and hyphenated words are not allowed.

14 words—good
21 words—great
27 words or more—fantastic

T R O W E L

Word Spiral

Starting from 1, fill in the grid in a clockwise direction with four-letter words. The last letter of each word becomes the first letter of the next word. If you have correctly filled in the grid, there should be a seven-letter key word reading across from 8.

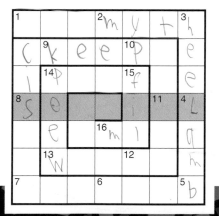

1. Baby's carriage
2. Legend
3. Foot part
4. Young sheep
5. Prejudice
6. Painful
7. God of love
8. Ill

9. Retain
10. Wan
11. Compass point
12. Defrost
13. Cried
14. Minor quarrel
15. Movie
16. Miserly

Key word clue: **Type of dog**

Word Wise

The words below may sound familiar, but do you know what they mean?

LAPIDARY

A Gem-cutter

B Student of the Lapp race

C Surgeon

IRASCIBLE

A Unalterable

B Irritable

C Unreasonable

NOVENA

A Recurring every ninth year

B Nine-day devotion

C Anticipate

TANGENT

A Touchable

B Line cutting a circle

C Line touching a curve

Remember When...

The statements on the left all refer to one year in the twentieth century, the statements on the right to another. Can you guess the years?

Rajiv Ghandi was assassinated.

The Birmingham (UK) Six were freed from jail.

Paul Keating unseated Bob Hawke as Prime Minister of Australia.

Operation Desert Storm took place.

A coup in Moscow precipitated the dissolution of the Soviet Union.

Gulf of Tonkin incident between US and North Vietnam.

Nelson Mandela was sentenced to life imprisonment.

Cassius Clay won the world heavyweight boxing championship.

Olympic games in Tokyo broadcast worldwide by satellite.

Peter Sellers married Britt Ekland.

Word Fit

The following words can be fitted into the grid on the opposite page. One word has already been inserted to give you a start.

4 letters	5 letters	6 letters	9 letters
ALSO	ARENA	APPEAL	BLOSSOMED
ARCH	DEMON	COSMOS	CHILDHOOD
ONUS	DODGE	MERINO	EPHEMERAL
OPEN	GIRTH	NORMAL	ESTABLISH
OPUS	HAPPY		GOLDSMITH
PASS	INANE		PRIMARILY
TINY	INURE		SUBMARINE
UGLY	SCOOP		SUCCESSOR
	SOPPY		
	YOUTH		

25

Mini Quiz

1. Who wrote and directed the film *High Hopes* in 1988?

2. Which country's name, in its native language, means 'Land of the Long White Cloud'?

3. What was the nationality of the artist Paul Klee?

4. In which novel is Yossarian a main character?

5. Which disease is popularly called 'the itch'?

Clockword

The solutions from 1 to 12 are all six-letter words ending with the letter T in the center. Moving clockwise from 1, the letters in the outer circle will spell out the name of a US vocalist who sang with The 4 Seasons.

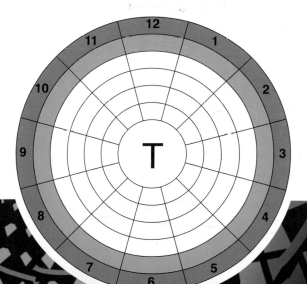

1. Polecat
2. Tourist town
3. Kidnap
4. Least old
5. Chess piece
6. Complete
7. Range
8. Fabric
9. Quantity
10. Lasso
11. Finch
12. Offend

Wordspiral

Starting at 1, fill in the grid in a clockwise direction with four-letter words. The last letter of each word becomes the first letter of the next word. If you have correctly filled in the grid there should be a seven-letter key word reading across from 8.

1. Cooking fat
2. Moist
3. Scheme
4. Without feeling
5. Ale
6. Hasty
7. Aid
8. Jetty

9. Gemstone
10. Toy (hyphenated)
11. Responsibility
12. Smack
13. Indigent
14. Rebellion
15. Roman garment
16. Female relative

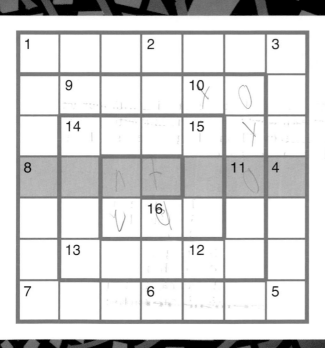

Key word clue:
Flat-bottomed boat
or British card game

Crossword

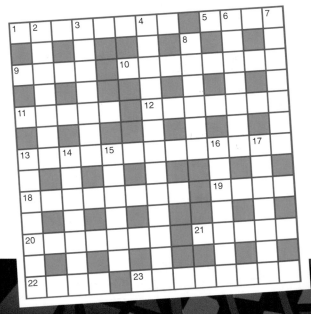

ACROSS

1. Method of musical performance denoted by a dot over the note. (8)
5. The derived SI unit of power. (4)
9 and 21 across. Author of the play *Barefoot in the Park*. (4, 5)
10. Spanish island whose capital is Santa Cruz. (8)
11. Nancy ---, golfer who won the 1985 USLPGA title. (5)
12. European republic whose capital is Reykjavik. (7)
13. American musical based on the play *Romeo and Juliet*. (4, 4, 5)
18. 1874 novel by Anthony Trollope. (4, 4)
19. 1816 novel by Jane Austen. (4)
20. Thick soup containing clams or fish. (7)
21. See 9 across.
22. 1979 film directed by Roman Polanski based on a Thomas Hardy novel. (4)
23. 1993 Peter Weir film starring Jeff Bridges. (8)

DOWN

2. 1953 film for which Richard Burton was a Best Actor Oscar nominee. (3, 4)
3. Claudette --- Best Actress Oscar winner for *It Happened One Night*. (7)
4. 1948 play by J B Priestley. (3, 6, 4)
6. Musical instruction that a piece be performed in an agitated manner. (7)
7. Ms Weld, actress and former wife of Dudley Moore. (7)
8. In classical mythology, a Trojan prince and son of Aphrodite who escaped the fall of Troy. (6)
13. The cat *Felis silvestris*. (7)
14. Sarah Kemble --- English actress who died in 1831. (7)
15. British drink made of beer and lemonade. (6)
16. 1965 Sidney Lumet film starring Sean Connery. (3, 4)
17. Broad-leaved garlic, *Allium ursinum*, native to Asia and Europe. (7)

Celebrity Wordmatch

Find a word that can follow the word on the left and precede the word on the right. When you have filled in all the answers, the name of a celebrity can be read from top to bottom in one of the lines.

HEAD							TIME
POP							BOX
HALF							BALL
BOY							SHIP
IVY							TABLE
YELLOW							COW
CHESS							GAME
DINNER							WINE
DEEP							FRAME
TURN							NECK
PEANUT							FINGERS
OLD							STROKE

Number Box

16	1	2	13
	9	11	
	6		
4	15		

Use all the numbers from 1 to 16 to fill in the spaces in the box. Each row across, each column down, and each diagonal from corner to corner must contain four numbers that add up to the same total.

Impossible Puzzles

Test your gray matter with these metal puzzles. The aim for all is to separate the pieces from the initial set. If at first you don't succeed read the steps for the answers.

Circle Pyramid

If you didn't manage to work this out on your own, then here is the secret. It's not as easy as it might look!

1. Arrange the pieces so that they are facing the same way as in the picture.

2. Slide the circle in the direction of the arrow, against the triangular piece.

3. The pieces should be separate now

Oblong Puzzler

This puzzler is guaranteed to get you in a twist! But don't fear, just follow our step-by-step instructions to discover the solution.

1. Make sure all the pieces are facing the same way as in the picture.

1.

2. Turn the left-hand oblong to the right, so that it looks like this picture.

3. Slide the oblongs in the direction of the arrows, and the pieces should come apart.

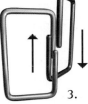

3.

4. Make sure you put it back correctly afterward, before challenging anyone else!

Bermuda Triangle

In this puzzle, you don't have to lose a triangle, you have to turn two joined triangles into two separate ones.

1. Arrange the pieces as in the picture.

2. Turn one of the triangles away from the other at a right angle, as shown.

3. Slide the triangle that you turned away, downward, in the direction of the arrow.

1.

3.

Unbroken

This, as yet, unbroken piece is about to be broken by you.

1. Start with the pieces facing the same way as in the picture.

2. Twist the left-hand piece 180 degrees in the direction of the arrow, as shown.

3. The pieces will simply come apart.

1.

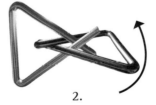

2.

Ring of Fire

These rings aren't really made of fire, but it is a hot trick.

1.

1. Hold the two pieces as shown in the picture.

2. Turn both rings backward in the direction of the arrows, so the rings are almost at right angles to each other.

2.

3. Slide the rings in the direction of the arrows, and they should come apart.

3.

Curly Wurly

This one will boggle your mind, and is more complex than the Ring of Fire.

1. Make sure you start with the pieces facing the same way as shown in the picture.

2. Move the right-hand piece in the direction of the arrow.

3. Keep twisting the piece in the same direction, then simply pull them apart.

1.

2.

Mixed up Puzzler

This is a more difficult puzzle, so there is no shame at peeking at the solution.

1. Arrange the pieces as shown in the diagram.

2. Twist the right-hand piece in the direction of the arrow, so that part B goes under part A and the right piece flips upside down.

3. Then simply pull tip D through the loop of tip B, and the pieces should come apart.

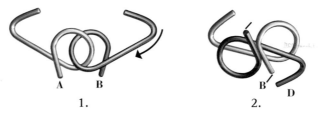

1.

2.

Broken Links

Another tricky one, but strangely satisfying once mastered.

1. Arrange the pieces as in the picture.

2. Move the circle down, as shown.

3. Move the oblong back so it is at a right angle to the circle, then move the oblong down, in the direction of the arrow.

4. They should come apart.

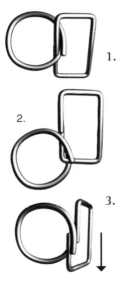

Tricky Puzzler

This one's very tricky.

1. Position the puzzles as shown, then move the right-hand piece in the direction of the arrow.

2. Keep moving the right-hand piece around, so that tip A goes through the loop of the left-hand piece.

3. Push the right-hand piece as directed, so that the two loops overlap.

4. Finally, push tip B over tip C and the pieces will separate.

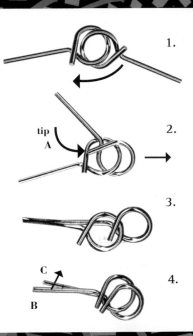

Solutions

CELEBRITY WORDMATCH page 4

CANDID	C	A	M	E	R	A	MAN
CHIP	B	O	A	R	D		ROOM
DARK	H	O	R	S	E		POWER
HIGH	R	O	L	L	E	R	BLADES
FIRST	B	L	O	O	D		BROTHER
ROMAN	C	A	N	D	L	E	STICK
CARD	T	A	B	L	E		TENNIS
BLUF	M	U	R	D	E	R	MYSTERY
SLEEPING	B	E	A	U	T	Y	SPOT
PANAMA	C	A	N	A	L		BOAT
LIBERTY	B	O	D	I	C	E	RIPPER
PAPER	P	R	O	F	I	T	MARGIN

IMPOSSIPUZZLE page 5

7119140625

36 voted

84 cents, $1.00, and $1.12

CLOCKWORD page 6

1. Method	5. Itched	9. Island
2. Impend	6. Expand	10. Varied
3. Needed	7. Demand	11. Ensued
4. Nudged	8. Rotund	12. Regard

Celebrity: Minnie Driver

MINI QUIZ page 7

1. Cutty Sark
2. Hispaniola
3. Jack Benny
4. Leo
5. Texas

CODEWORD page 9

1 T	2 D	3 P	4 R	5 A	6 S	7 E	8 I	9 N	10 K	11 V	12 H	13 L
14 G	15 C	16 B	17 U	18 O	19 M	20 X	21	22	23	24	25	26

WORD WISE page 10

Gillie A Scottish manservant
Brisket A joint of meat
Volition Exercise one's will
Prevaricate Evade the truth

CLOCKWORD page 11

1. Salmon
2. Tavern
3. Eleven
4. Violin
5. Inborn
6. Enjoin
7. Warden
8. Orphan
9. Notion
10. Damson
11. Ensign
12. Raisin

Celebrity: Stevie Wonder

CROSSWORD page 12

NUMBERWORD page 14

WORD PUZZLE page 16

R	E	A	R	H	O	N	E	S	A
H	R	B	T	O	R	E	D	A	C
I	G	O	R	L	N	R	O	Y	L
N	A	N	O	L	I	F	F	E	Y
E	N	C	D	I	L	M	N	V	D
X	T	H	A	M	E	S	T	I	E
F	I	R	N	U	N	G	L	E	C
N	B	O	U	R	S	E	I	N	E
G	E	L	B	E	N	G	N	T	N
P	R	E	E	S	T	R	I	O	K

1. Danube
2. Seine
3. Clyde
4. Rhine
5. Thames
6. Elbe
7. Liffey
8. Tiber
9. Rhone
10. Nile

MINI QUIZ page 17

1. Motown
2. Salmon
3. Zurich
4. India
5. Kurt Vonnegut

CODEWORD page 18

1 N	2 A	3 L	4 I	5 H	6 P	7 T	8 R	9 O	10 S	11 E	12 J	13 C
14 U	15 W	16 K	17 D	18 F	19 V	20 G	21 Y	22 M	23 X	24	25	26

WORD SCRAMBLER page 20

DIGEST deist, die, dies, diet, diets, dig, digs, dis, edit, edits, get, gets, gist, ides, its, set, side, sit, site, sited, ted, teds, tide, tides, tie, ties, tied, tig.

TROWEL let, lor, lore, lot, low, lower, ore, owl, owlet, owe, roe, role, rot, rote, row, rowel, toe, tor, tore, tow, towel, tower, two, welt, wet, woe, wort, wore, wrote.

WORD SPIRAL page 21

1. Pram
2. Myth
3. Heel
4. Lamb
5. Bias
6. Sore
7. Eros
8. Sick
9. Keep
10. Pale
11. East
12. Thaw
13. Wept
14. Tiff
15. Film
16. Mean

Key Word Solution: Spaniel

WORDWISE page 22

Lapidary Gem-cutter
Novena Nine-day devotion
Irascible Irritable
Tangent Line touching a curve

REMEMBER WHEN... page 23

Left: 1991   Right: 1964

WORD FIT page 24

S		B		G	O	L	D	S	M	I	T	H
U	G	L	Y		N		E		E		I	
C		O		S	U	B	M	A	R	I	N	E
C	O	S	M	O	S		O		I		Y	
E		S		P		I	N	A	N	E		E
S	C	O	O	P		N			O	P	U	S
S		M		Y	O	U	T	H		H		T
O	P	E	N			R		A	R	E	N	A
R		D	O	D	G	E		P		M		B
	A		R		I		A	P	P	E	A	L
P	R	I	M	A	R	I	L	Y		R		I
	C		A		T		S		P	A	S	S
C	H	I	L	D	H	O	O	D			L	H

MINI QUIZ page 26

1. Mike Leigh; 2. New Zealand (Aotearoa in Maori); 3. Swiss; 4. *Catch 22*; 5. Scabies

CLOCKWORD page 27

1. Ferret; 2. Resort; 3. Abduct; 4. Newest; 5. Knight; 6. Intact; 7. Extent; 8. Velvet; 9. Amount; 10. Lariat; 11. Linnet; 12. Insult

Celebrity: Frankie Valli

46

WORDSPIRAL page 28

Key word solution: Pontoon

1.	Lard	9.	Ruby
2.	Damp	10.	Yo-yo
3.	Plan	11.	Onus
4.	Numb	12.	Slap
5.	Beer	13.	Poor
6.	Rash	14.	Riot
7.	Help	15.	Toga
8.	Pier	16.	Aunt

CROSSWORD page 30

ACROSS: 1. Staccato; 5. Watt; 9. Neil; 10. Tenerife; 11. Lopez; 12. Iceland; 13. *West Side Story*; 18. Lady Anna; 19. Emma; 20. Chowder; 21. Simon; 22. Tess; 23. Fearless. **DOWN:** 2. The Robe; 3. Colbert; 4. The Linden Tree; 6. Agitato; 7. Tuesday; 8. Aeneas; 13. Wildcat; 14. Siddons; 15. Shandy; 16. The Hill; 17. Ramsons.

CELEBRITY WORDMATCH page 32

HEAD	I	N	J	U	R	Y	TIME
POP	■	M	U	S	I	C	BOX
HALF	V	O	L	L	E	Y	BALL
BOY	F	R	I	E	N	D	SHIP
IVY	L	E	A	G	U	E	TABLE
YELLOW	J	E	R	S	E	Y	COW
CHESS	■	B	O	A	R	D	GAME
DINNER	T	A	B	L	E	■	WINE
DEEP	F	R	E	E	Z	E	FRAME
TURN	T	U	R	T	L	E	NECK
PEANUT	B	U	T	T	E	R	FINGERS
OLD	M	A	S	T	E	R	STROKE

NUMBER BOX page 33

16	3	2	13
5	10	11	8
9	6	7	12
4	15	14	1

solutions to 3d puzzles
pages 34-42

The puzzles featured on pages 12-33 are supplied by Central Press Features Ltd.

Conclusion

If you've completed the vast array of puzzles
within this book, then your brain cells are
probably in need of a well-deserved rest. So why
not sit back and share some of the trickier
puzzles with the rest of the family?

A Season of Sight Words
SPRING Treehouse Time!

Y0-CCB-859

old
from

by Shannon Penney
Illustrated by Luanne Marten

Scholastic Inc.

ISBN 978-0-545-34441-8

14 13 12 11 10   20/0

Printed in the U.S.A.   132
First printing, March 2013

Where did you get this **old** stuff **from**?

I got these **old** boards **from** my dad.

I got these **old** nails **from** my mom.

I got these **old** tools **from** my brother.

Let's take everything to the **old** tree.

It is nice to have help **from** friends!